PRIMARY WORD WORK

BOOK 1

Louis Fidge
Sarah Lindsay

Collins Educational
An imprint of HarperCollins*Publishers*

Published by Collins Educational
An imprint of HarperCollinsPublishers Ltd
77-85 Fulham Palace Road
London W6 8JB

First published 1998

ISBN 0 00 302486 5

Illustrations by Maggie Brand, Rob Englebright, Belinda Evans, Bethan Matthews, Andrew Midgely, Rhiannon Powell.

British Library Cataloguing in Publication Data
A catalogue record for this book is available from the British Library.

Cover illustration: Bethan Matthews
Editor: Janet Swarbrick
Designer: Celia Hart

Printed by Scotprint, Musselburgh

Acknowledgments
The authors and publishers wish to thank the following for permission to use copyright material:

Faber and Faber Ltd for 'Teacher said ...' from *Magic Mirror and Other Poems for Children* by Judith Nicholls, 1985.

Every effort has been made to trace the copyright holders but if any have been inadvertently overlooked the publishers will be pleased to make the necessary arrangement at the first opportunity.

Contents

Unit		Page
1	Using a dictionary	4
2	Adding **ing**	6
3	Using context clues	8
4	Spelling with **le**	10
5	Using a thesaurus	12
6	Prefixes (1)	14
7	Synonyms	16
8	Adding **er** and **est**	18
9	Dialogue words	20
10	Singular and plural	22
	Progress Test A	24
11	Alphabetical order	26
12	Silent letters	28
13	Using guide words	30
14	Compound words	32
15	Antonyms	34
16	Suffixes	36
17	Homonyms	38
18	The apostrophe	40
19	Common expressions	42
20	Prefixes (2)	44
	Progress Test B	46

Using a dictionary

Dictionaries are arranged in **alphabetical order**.

Dictionaries give us the **definitions** (meanings) of words.

This page comes near the end of my dictionary.

Some words have more than one definition.

vanish	To disappear suddenly.
vehicle	A machine such as a car, bus or lorry that carries people or goods from place to place.
volume	1. One of a set of books. 2. The amount of space filled by something. 3. The loudness of a sound.
vulture	A large bird that feeds on dead animals.

Dictionaries help us **check spellings**.

vulcher

Have I spelt this word correctly?

Practice

Copy and complete these sentences.

1. Dictionaries are arranged in a_____ o_____.
2. Dictionaries give us the d_____ of words.
3. Dictionaries help us check the s_____ of words.

More to think about

Use a dictionary. Look up these words. Write a definition for each word.

These words are found at the beginning of the dictionary.

1. a) acrobat   b) dove   c) harpoon   d) beaver

These words are found in the middle of the dictionary.

2. a) kilt   b) linen
   c) mustard   d) newt

These words all come near the end of the dictionary.

3. a) poison   b) wreath
   c) thimble   d) syrup

Now try these

1. Copy these definitions. Use a dictionary to complete the words.
   a) A bird that cannot fly.   os _ _ _ _ _ _
   b) This makes things look bigger.   micro _ _ _ _ _ _
   c) A large church.   ab _ _ _ _

2. Use a dictionary. Write a definition for each of these words.
   a) restaurant   b) panda   c) statue   d) burglar

3. Use a dictionary to check the spellings of these words. If the word is misspelt, write it out correctly.
   a) parashoot   b) pyramid   c) sholder   d) electrisity

Adding ing

When **ing** is added to short words, sometimes the last letter of the word is doubled.

Check the words **swim**, **sing** and **sleep**.

Is the second to last letter a vowel **a, e, i, o** or **u**?

Yes

No

Is it a single vowel?

Add **ing**
sing ⟶ singing

Yes

No

Double the last letter
and add **ing**
swim ⟶ swimming

Add **ing**
sleep ⟶ sleeping

If a verb ends in **w, x** or **y**, just add **ing**.
blow ⟶ blowing

Practice

Copy these words and add ing.

1. cook

2. shop

3. kick

4. bat

5. break

6. hop

More to think about

Look at the picture. Write a list of all the actions you can see. The list has been started for you.

winning
hopping

Now try these

Copy and complete the table.

beg	begging
clap	
talk	
grow	
stand	
break	
bat	
relax	
fly	

Using context clues

When we don't know the meaning of a word, we can sometimes get **clues** from a picture or the words around it.

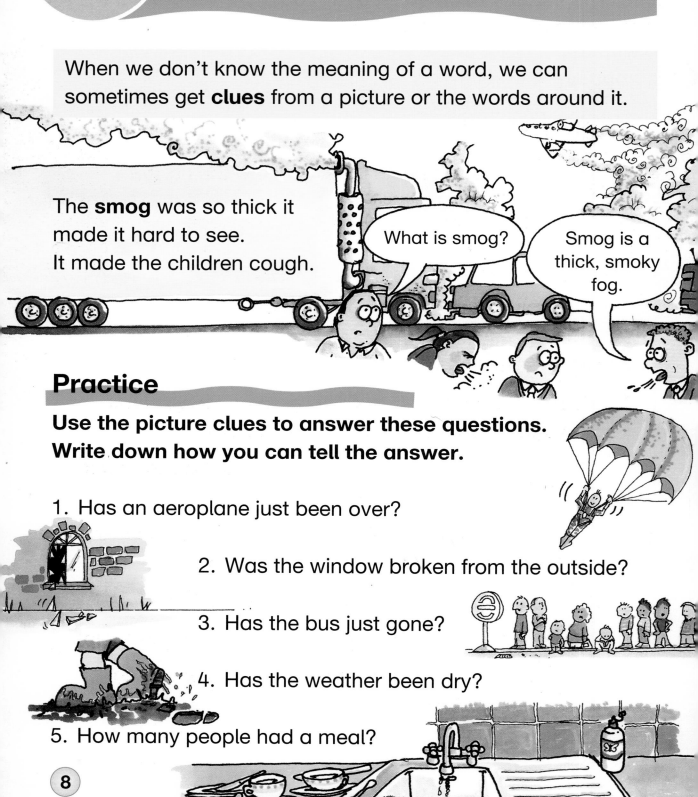

The **smog** was so thick it made it hard to see.
It made the children cough.

What is smog?

Smog is a thick, smoky fog.

Practice

Use the picture clues to answer these questions.
Write down how you can tell the answer.

1. Has an aeroplane just been over?

2. Was the window broken from the outside?

3. Has the bus just gone?

4. Has the weather been dry?

5. How many people had a meal?

More to think about

Write the meaning of each underlined word.
Check your answers in a dictionary. Use the pictures
and sentences to help you.

1. The sun began to sink below the <u>horizon</u>.

2. The man was lying in a <u>hammock</u>.

3. The monk lived in a <u>monastery</u>.

Now try these

Work out and write the meaning of each underlined
word. Check your answers in a dictionary.

1. The author sent the publishers a copy of his new book,
   but he kept a <u>duplicate</u> of it for himself.

2. The teacher knew something was wrong when she saw
   Lewis <u>gesticulating</u> wildly.

3. When you plant seeds, you must <u>saturate</u> them first.

4. The only form of <u>illumination</u> in the castle was oil lamps.

5. The police officer did not believe the burglar's <u>account</u>
   of what happened.

Spelling with le

Many words end in **le**.

candle   handle

rect<u>ang</u>**le**   str<u>ang</u>**le**

b<u>ubb</u>**le**   r<u>ubb</u>**le**

These **le** words can be split into groups with similar spelling patterns.

Practice

Copy the table. Write the word in the box in the correct column.

| crumble | bangle | mumble | tangle | rumble | sprinkle |
| wrinkle | scramble | ramble | jangle | stumble | twinkle |

-umble	-angle	-amble	-inkle

More to think about

Work out the clues to find words that end in le.

1. Often put on top of stewed apple
   or rhubarb to make a pudding.   cr_____

2. Used when the lights go out.   c_____

3. A slight fall.   st_____

4. Two of the same things.   d_____

5. To scatter droplets of water.   spr_____

6. Not speaking clearly.   m_____

7. Easy.   s_____

8. The sound leaves make in the wind. r_____

Now try these

1. Find six hidden **le** words in this wordsearch.
   Write the words out neatly. Learn how to spell them.

o	r	u	s	t	l	e	s
g	c	p	a	e	l	m	c
a	a	n	g	l	e	t	r
n	n	f	j	t	n	a	a
k	d	l	m	s	k	q	m
l	l	l	t	u	r	u	b
e	e	s	e	r	h	k	l
z	k	s	i	n	g	l	e

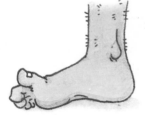

2. Write six sentences.
   Use one **le**
   word from the
   wordsearch in
   each sentence.

UNIT 5 Using a thesaurus

A **thesaurus** is a book that contains synonyms. **Synonyms** are words that have **similar meanings**.

A thesaurus is arranged in **alphabetical order**.

main word	type of word	synonyms

tall	*adj.*	big, lofty, high
tank	*n.*	1. armoured vehicle, combat car
		2. reservoir, cistern, vat
teach	*v.*	inform, tell, instruct, educate, show, explain
terrible	*adj.*	horrible, vile, frightful, fearful, dreadful
thaw	*v.*	melt, dissolve, defrost
thief	*n.*	burglar, crook, robber, pilferer
thirsty	*adj.*	arid, dry, parched

adj. = adjective   *n.* = noun   *v.* = verb

This is a page from my thesaurus.

Practice

1. Copy and complete these sentences.
   a) A thesaurus is a book that contains s_____.
   b) Synonyms are words with similar m_____.

2. Use the thesaurus page above. Answer these questions.
   a) What are the three synonyms for the word 'tall'?
   b) Which two words mean the same as 'melt'?
   c) Which word has two different meanings?
   d) Which of the words are nouns?

More to think about

Copy the sentences. Replace each underlined word with a synonym. Use the thesaurus page on page 12 to help you.

1. Mother tried to <u>teach</u> Jo how to tie a knot.

2. The icicles began to <u>thaw</u>.

3. The <u>thief</u> broke into the house.

4. The <u>tall</u> giant climbed down the beanstalk.

5. The <u>tank</u> lumbered noisily along.

6. Tom looked out of the window at the <u>terrible</u> weather.

Now try these

1. Use a thesaurus. Write a sentence for each of these words.
   a) soak   b) nudge   c) blot out   d) consume
   e) punch   f) sparkle   g) guard   h) wonderful

2. Now use the thesaurus to find some synonyms for each word.

   a) soak – saturate, drench, drown

Prefixes (1)

A **prefix** is a group of letters added to the **beginning** of a word. A **prefix** changes the meaning of a word in a particular way.

like

dislike

cover

uncover

A word changes to its **antonym (opposite meaning)** if the prefix **dis** or **un** is added to it.

visit

revisit

The prefix **re** means 'done again'.

Practice

1. Match the correct word to each picture.

| happy | zip | cover | equal |

a)

b) $4 = 2 + 2$

c)

d)

2. Now write the antonym (opposite meaning) of each word by adding the prefix un.

More to think about

Copy the story. Fill in each gap with a suitable word from the box. Circle the prefix in each word. The first one has been done for you.

> If you don't understand a word, look it up in your dictionary.

return	unhappy	reunited	uncertain
disappeared	disobey	uneven	

Ben looked un)happy. Lorna, his dog, had run away. Ben was _____ about what he should do. Should he _____ home or should he stay? Suddenly, he heard his mum call. He didn't want to _____ her but he didn't want to leave Lorna either.

   "Where have you _____ to?" shouted his mum. "Lorna has come home but where are you?"

   Ben couldn't believe his ears. He raced over the _____ playground and was soon happily _____ with Lorna.

Now try these

1. Copy the table. Write three words in each column. One word has been done for you. Use a dictionary to help you.

un	dis	de	re	pre
	disobey			

2. Now choose five words from the table. Make up a sentence for each word.

Synonyms

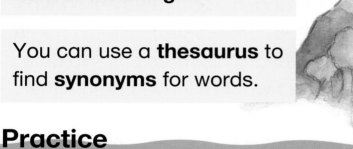

The giant was **huge**. His wife was also **enormous**.

Synonyms are words with **similar meanings**.

You can use a **thesaurus** to find **synonyms** for words.

Practice

1. Match each word in Set A with its synonym in Set B. The first one has been done for you. *big – large*

Set A	big	break	like	nice	nasty

Set B	bad	smash	large	enjoy	pleasant

2. Copy these sentences. Replace the underlined word with a synonym. Use a thesaurus to help you.
   a) Emma lives in a <u>big</u> house.
   b) A vase will <u>break</u> if you drop it.
   c) I <u>like</u> playing games.
   d) It was a <u>nice</u> day.
   e) There was a <u>nasty</u> smell coming from the dustbin.

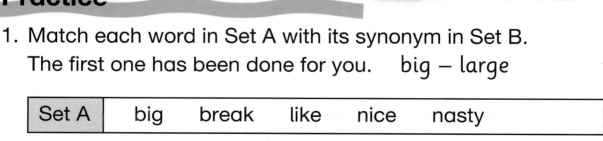

More to think about

1. Copy these sets of synonyms. Underline the odd word out.
   a) good kind friendly burst   b) cold huge icy frosty
   c) eat happy chew gobble   d) fair look stare peep

2. Copy the sentences. Choose one of
   these words to fill each gap.

looked	stared	peeped

   a) The lady _____ in amazement at the girl with pink hair.
   b) The boy _____ through the keyhole.
   c) I _____ at my shopping list to see what I needed.

3. Make up three sentences to show the
   difference between these synonyms.

toddled	jogged	galloped

Now try these

1. Use a thesaurus to help you find the missing synonym.
   a) speak   t _ _ _   b) hurry   r _ _ _
   c) observe l _ _ _   d) beautiful p _ _ _ _ _
   e) locate   f _ _ _   f) stroll   w _ _ _

2. Choose one synonym from each pair above. Make up a
   sentence for each word you choose.

3. Use a thesaurus. Find three synonyms for each of
   these words.
   a) go b) happy c) hot d) nice e) good f) little

Adding **er** and **est**

When **er** or **est** is added to short words,
sometimes the last letter of the word doubles.

Check the words **sing**, **short**, **run**, **fit** and **sweet**.

Is the second to last letter a vowel **a**, **e**, **i, o** or **u**?

Yes   No

Is it a single vowel?

Add **er** or **est**.
sing ⟶ **singer**
short ⟶ **shorter** or **shortest**

Yes   No

Double the last letter
and add **er** or **est**.
run ⟶ **runner**
fit ⟶ **fitter** or **fittest**

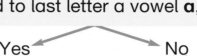

Add **er** or **est**.
sweet ⟶ **sweeter** or **sweetest**

When a word ends in **y**, it changes to **i** when
er or **est** is added.

 smell**y**   smell**ier**   smell**iest**

Practice

Copy these words. Add er and est to each word.

1. big ⟶ bigger ⟶ biggest   2. hot   3. cold

4. sad   5. tall   6. fast

More to think about

Copy the sentences. Add er and est
to the underlined word. Write the
words in the gaps.

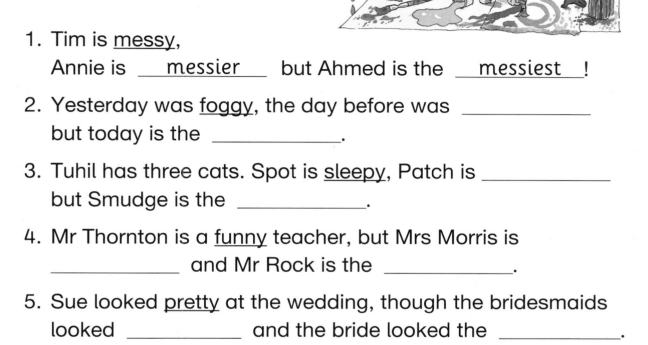

1. Tim is <u>messy</u>,
   Annie is ___messier___ but Ahmed is the ___messiest___ !

2. Yesterday was <u>foggy</u>, the day before was _____
   but today is the _____ .

3. Tuhil has three cats. Spot is <u>sleepy</u>, Patch is _____
   but Smudge is the _____ .

4. Mr Thornton is a <u>funny</u> teacher, but Mrs Morris is
   _____ and Mr Rock is the _____ .

5. Sue looked <u>pretty</u> at the wedding, though the bridesmaids
   looked _____ and the bride looked the _____ .

Now try these

1. Correct the words that are spelt incorrectly.
   Say why you have changed them.

sunnest	hotest	bigger	sleepiest
	mader	runer	stonier

2. Now write a short story about an adventure on a beach.
   Use all the words in the box. Make sure they are
   spelt correctly.

Dialogue words

Dialogue words describe how people **say** things.

Teacher said,

"You can use
mumbled and muttered,
groaned, grumbled and uttered,
professed, droned or stuttered
... but don't use SAID!"

"You can use
rant or recite,
yell, yodel or snort,
bellow, murmur or moan,
you can grunt or just groan
... but don't use SAID!"

... SAID my teacher.

Judith Nichols

Practice

Copy the sentences. Underline the dialogue words.
The first one has been done for you.

1. "What are you doing?" Mrs Shahidi <u>asked</u>.

2. "I am looking for my gerbil," replied Tom.

3. "Help! There's a large rat in my bag!" Samir shrieked.

4. "Don't worry. It's the gerbil!" exclaimed Anna.

5. "Perhaps it is looking for something to eat," Tara added.

6. "Put the gerbil back in the cage and get on with your work," Mrs Shahidi said.

More to think about

Copy the sentences. Choose the best dialogue word for each one.

replied	exclaimed	asked	added

1. "Where does a baby ape sleep?" Kevin _____ .
   "In an apricot!" his father _____ with a grin.

2. "What a lovely view!" _____ Kirsty.
   "You can see a long way," _____ Sam.

Now try these

1. Use a thesaurus. Find a synonym for each of these words.
   a) whisper b) call   c) say   d) shout   e) exclaim
   f) cry   g) ask   h) reply i) sigh   j) mutter

2. Choose a page from a book that has speech in it. Write down all the dialogue words.

UNIT 10 Singular and plural

Singular means **one**.
Plural means **more than one**.

To make a word **plural**, we usually just add an **s**.

To make a word that ends in s, x, ch or sh **plural**, we add **es**.

one goat

two goat**s**

one box

two box**es**

Practice

Write the plural of each word.

1. boat

boats

2. toy

toys ~~tos~~

3. cow

cows

4. tree

trees

5. dog

6. fish

7. flag

8. pen

More to think about

1. Write what you see in each picture. Be careful, some things are **singular** and some are **plural**.

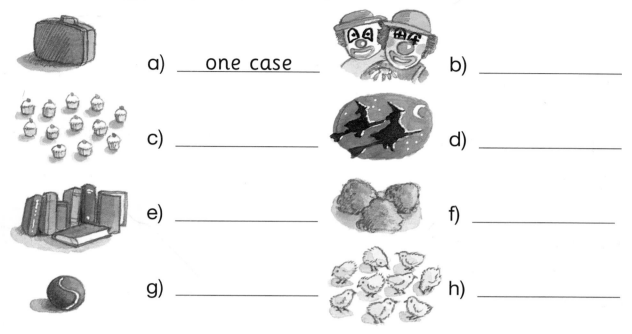

a) <u>one case</u>

b) _____

c) _____

d) _____

e) _____

f) _____

g) _____

h) _____

2. Choose three of the pictures. Write a sentence about each picture.

Now try these

Change the five words in the box to plurals. Write a short story about a farmer who can't find his pet goat. Use the plurals in your story.

| field |
| cow |
| carrot |
| ditch |
| dog |

Progress Test A

1. Write what you think the underlined word in each sentence means.

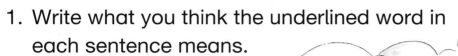

   a) The passengers <u>abandoned</u> the sinking ship.
   b) The wicked <u>ogre</u> locked the princess in a tower.
   c) The paintbrush had no <u>bristles</u> left.

2. Copy these words and add **ing** to each.
   a) leap   b) skip   c) jump   d) hop
   e) look   f) brush   g) tug   h) stoop

3. Use a dictionary. Write a definition for each of these words.

   a) magic   b) bramble   c) anchor   d) peak   e) glossary

4. Complete each word using **kle**, **ble** or **gle**.
   a) gur _ _ _   b) spar _ _ _   c) bub _ _ _

5. Match each word in Set A to its synonym in Set B.

Set A	shout	nice	receive	run	wet	fast

Set B	damp	pleasant	speedy	race	get	yell

6. Complete each word using the prefix **un** or **dis**.

   a) ___appear   b) ___wrap   c) ___tie   d) ___may

7. Use a thesaurus. Write a synonym for each of these words.

   a) wicked   b) ending   c) small   d) gloomy   e) walk

8. Copy and complete this table.

big	bigger	biggest
small		
fat		
loud		
wet		

9. Choose the best dialogue word to complete each sentence.

shouted	whispered	groaned	stuttered

   a) "I don't feel very well," the sick child _____.

   b) "Help! I've been robbed!" _____ the shopkeeper.

   c) "Don't wake up the baby," Mrs Samir _____.

   d) "It's a g… g… g… ghost," _____ the terrified boy.

10. Complete each sentence with the singular or plural word.

   a) One dish but two _____.

   b) One fox but two _____.

   d) One bucket but two _____.

   c) One dragon but two _____.

   f) One _____ but two churches.

   d) One _____ but two candles.

   h) One _____ two wishes.

25

UNIT 11 Alphabetical order

It is important to know the **correct order** of the **letters** in the **alphabet**. Many books contain words in **alphabetical order**.

alligator   **b**ear   **c**amel   **sh**eep   **squ**irrel   **st**ork

These animals are arranged in **alphabetical order** according to their **first** letters.

These animals are arranged in **alphabetical order** according to their **second** letters.

Practice

1. Copy and complete these sentences.
   - a) **c** comes after _____.
   - b) **t** comes after _____.
   - c) **o** comes after _____.
   - d) **a** comes before _____.
   - e) **k** comes before _____.
   - f) **r** comes before _____.

2. Copy and fill in the missing letters.
   - a) a b c __ __
   - b) n o p __ __
   - c) s t u v __ __

3. Write these letters in alphabetical order.
   - a) b d e a c
   - b) w y u x v
   - c) h k g j i
   - d) y f l
   - e) o d g
   - f) t a c

More to think about

1. List these animals in alphabetical order.
   a) tiger deer fox
   b) hedgehog monkey goat
   c) rabbit ape elephant
   d) kangaroo cat gerbil
   e) jaguar lion tiger zebra
   f) reindeer yak ox giraffe

2. Rewrite these children's names in alphabetical order.

a)
Jessica

Amy

Waka

Nasir

Emma

b)
Thomas

Mohammed

Jacob

Diraj

Edward

Now try these

1. List these words in alphabetical order.

   a)

   clown   chemist   caretaker   conductor

   b) doctor driver detective diver
   c) Bulgaria Belgium Britain Botswana
   d) spaghetti sweets soup salt strawberries

2. Use a dictionary. Write the name of an animal
   beginning with the following letters.
   a) co   b) ch   c) cr   d) ca

Silent letters

When some words are read aloud, some of the letters do not have a sound. These letters are called **silent letters**.

Read these words aloud.

knot		**k**not
wreck		**w**reck
bomb		bom**b**

The letter in **red** is the silent letter.

Practice

Write these words carefully. Say each word aloud.
Circle the silent letter. The first one has been done for you.

1. ⓚnee

2. comb

3. wrap

4. write

5. knit

6. climb

7. crumb

8. sword

9. knock

More to think about

| lamb | knife | wren | sword | wrist | comb | doubt | knight |

1. Copy the table. Write the words from the box in the correct columns.

silent **b**	silent **k**	silent **w**
lamb		

2. Add three more words of your own to each column.

Now try these

1. Copy these words. Fill in the missing silent letters.

a) ___nife   b) clim___   c) ___nocker

d) ___riggle   e) g___ost   f) s___issors

g) ___our   h) com___   i) mus___le

2. Choose five of these words. Write a sentence for each word.

UNIT 13 Using guide words

In a dictionary there are usually two **guide words** at the top of each page. They help you find words more quickly and easily.

This tells you the first word on page 47.

crush	page 47	**cuddle**
crush	To squash or press something so hard that it is broken.	
cry	1. To let tears fall from your eyes. 2. To shout loudly.	
cube	A solid object with six equal square surfaces.	
cucumber	A long, green salad vegetable.	
cuddle	To put your arms closely around a person or animal you love.	

This tells you the last word on page 47.

Practice

Answer these questions.

1. Which is the first word on the dictionary page above?
2. Which is the last word on the page?
3. With which letter do all the words on the page begin?
4. Would the page above be near the beginning or the end of the dictionary?

More to think about

Copy and complete the sentences. Use a dictionary to help you.

When you have finished, write the words in alphabetical order.

1. A sh _ _ _ is a large fish that sometimes attacks people.
2. A str _ _ _ _ _ _ _ _ is a soft, red fruit.
3. A syc _ _ _ _ _ is a type of tree.
4. A sur _ _ _ _ is a doctor who performs operations.

Now try these

1. Match the guide words to the word that should appear on the same page.

spire to **spread**	well
heat to **helpless**	lock
weather to **whale**	splash
living to **lollipop**	track
towel to **travel**	purpose
public to **pyramid**	hedgehog

2. Think of a word that could fit between each of these guide words.

   a) shape _____ snooze   b) fly _____ friend
   c) bank _____ brush   d) pen _____ purse

Compound words

A **compound word** is made from two small words joined together.

playground

play + ground

Practice

Use a word from the box to make the compound word pictured.

| worm | driver | storm | ball | ache | flake | port | water |

1. foot _ball_

2. air _____

3. earth _____

4. rain _____

5. snow _____

6. screw _____

7. tooth _____

8. thunder _____

More to think about

1. Write the compound word shown by the pictures.

a) _____ + _____ = _____

b) _____ + _____ = _____

c) _____ + _____ = _____

d) _____ + _____ = _____

2. Now write four more compound words. For each word draw pictures of the two small words that make the compound word.

Now try these

Copy these compound words.
Split them into the two small words.
The first one has been done for you.

1. pineapple = ____pine____ + ____apple____

2. seaweed = _____ + _____

3. upset = _____ + _____

4. everyone = _____ + _____

5. funfair = _____ + _____

6. aircraft = _____ + _____

7. afternoon = _____ + _____

Antonyms

Antonyms are words that have opposite **meanings**

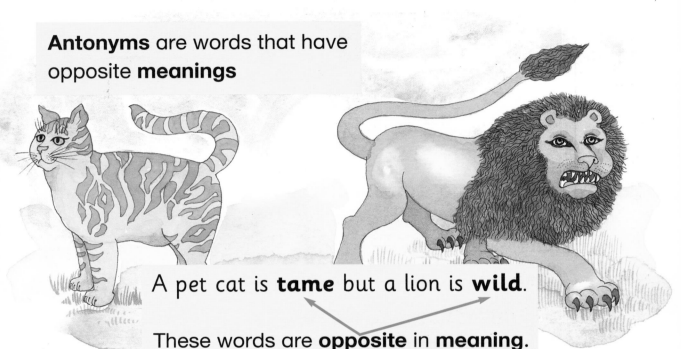

A pet cat is **tame** but a lion is **wild**.

These words are **opposite** in **meaning**.

Practice

Copy the words. Underline the pair of antonyms in each set.

1. fat <u>easy</u> <u>difficult</u>
2. nasty thin nice
3. full bent straight
4. hot near cold
5. up top down
6. rude wet polite wrong
7. smooth ugly beautiful short
8. blue expensive soft cheap
9. fat heavy thin rough

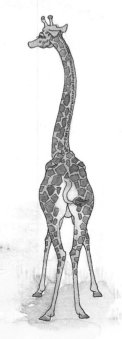

More to think about

Copy these sentences. Fill in each gap with a suitable antonym.

1. My hair is <u>curly</u> but Sam has _____ hair.

2. Tom is <u>noisy</u> but Ahmed is _____.

3. Pat is <u>polite</u> but Ben is _____.

4. Mr Drew walks <u>slowly</u> but his wife walks _____.

5. I like to <u>save</u> my money but Shirin likes to _____ hers.

6. The blue bag is <u>empty</u> but the red bag is _____.

Now try these

Rewrite these sentences. Change each underlined word to its antonym.

1. Our class is the <u>best</u> in the school.
2. My dog is very <u>obedient</u>.
3. Charlotte always comes to school <u>early</u>.
4. The rabbit <u>vanished</u> in a flash.
5. I looked for the <u>entrance</u>.
6. The judge said the man was <u>guilty</u>.

Suffixes

A **suffix** is a group of letters added to the **end** of a word.
A **suffix** changes the meaning of the word or the way it can be used.

quick + **ly**
= quickly

use + **ful**
= useful

weak + **ness**
= weakness

Some common **suffixes** are **ly**, **ful** and **ness**.

Joseph ran **quickly**.
The cloth was very **useful** when the paint was spilt!
My dad has a **weakness** for chocolate.

Practice

Write each word with its suffix separated.
The first one has been done for you.

1. smartly   =   _smart_   +   _ly_

2. thoughtful   =   _____   +   _____

3. painful   =   _____   +   _____

4. blindness   =   _____   +   _____

5. honestly   =   _____   +   _____

6. slowly   =   _____   +   _____

7. fitness   =   _____   +   _____

8. careful   =   _____   +   _____

More to think about

Match each word with its correct suffix. Remember, some words will match more than one suffix!

| ly | ful | ness |

Use a dictionary to help you.

hope   smart   dark   spite

blind   wonder

ill   quiet   kind

Now try these

1. Complete the sentences using words that end in **ly**, **ful** or **ness**. The first one has been done for you.

   a) If something doesn't move very quickly, it moves ___slowly___ .

   b) If a stone hits someone in the eye, it can cause b_____ .

   c) When Laura broke her arm, it was very p_____ .

   d) The bride looked l_____ at her wedding.

   e) Jack was c_____ when he decorated the cake.

2. Write four more sentences. Use a word ending in **ly**, **ful** or **ness** in each sentence. Underline the words with these suffixes.

UNIT 17 Homonyms

Homonyms are words that have the **same spelling**, but **different meanings**.

I gave a **wave** as I splashed in the **wave**.

Practice

Copy these sentences.
Underline the homonyms.

1. The pirate's treasure chest was full of gold.
   The pirate had a hairy chest.

2. My best pen was broken.
   You put sheep in a pen.

3. I spread jam on my bread.
   The car was stuck in a traffic jam.

4. There was no water in the tank.
   The army tank was very noisy.

More to think about

Copy these sentences.
Complete them with the most
suitable homonyms from the box.

match	calf	ring	bow

1. The girl had a _____ in her hair.
   The archer put an arrow in his _____.

2. On television there was a football _____.
   I struck a _____ to light the candle.

3. The lady wears a _____ on her finger.
   I heard the telephone _____ in the kitchen.

4. A baby cow is called a _____.
   The part of my leg between my knee and my ankle is
   my _____.

Now try these

Make up pairs of sentences using the homonyms below.
Remember the same homonym must have a different
meaning in each sentence.

Use a dictionary
to help if you wish.

a) palm   b) tie   c) fly
d) toast   e) skirt   f) patient
g) tear   h) quiver   i) lift

The apostrophe

Sometimes, words are joined together and letters are missed out. This makes one shorter word. These shortened words are called **contractions**.

is not ⟶ isn't

we will ⟶ we'll

We use an **apostrophe** to show where there are **missing letters.**

Practice

1. Copy these sentences. Underline each **contraction**.
   a) Dad <u>didn't</u> know where James had gone.
   b) "Don't do that," called the teacher.
   c) "I'll show you the way home," said Mum.
   d) "It's time for bed!" the babysitter called.
   e) Tuhil ate the sweets he shouldn't have found!

2. Now write out all the contractions as two words. The first one has been done for you.

   didn't ⟶ did not

More to think about

Copy the two lists. Match each
contraction with its longer form.

we'll	was not
you're	we will
didn't	should not
wasn't	it is
don't	you are
it's	we are
shouldn't	did not
can't	do not
haven't	can not
we're	have not

It's big

Now try these

1. Copy the words. Put the apostrophe in the correct place.
   - a) dont
   - b) couldnt
   - c) cant
   - d) its
   - e) weve
   - f) wouldnt
   - g) youre
   - h) wasnt
   - i) didnt

2. Make up four sentences. Use one contraction in
   each sentence.

I can't . . .

Common expressions

Every day we use **common expressions** ...

... of apology

... of greeting

... of surprise

... of warning

... of thanks

... of refusal

Practice

Copy these expressions. Say whether each is used for greeting someone or for saying goodbye.

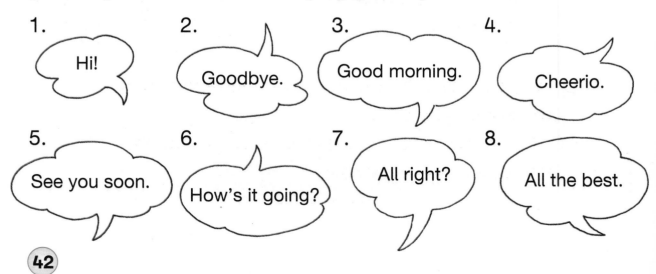

1. Hi!

2. Goodbye.

3. Good morning.

4. Cheerio.

5. See you soon.

6. How's it going?

7. All right?

8. All the best.

More to think about

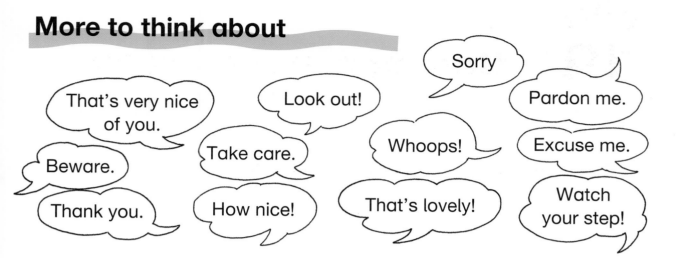

That's very nice of you.

Look out!

Sorry

Pardon me.

Beware.

Take care.

Whoops!

Excuse me.

Thank you.

How nice!

That's lovely!

Watch your step!

Copy the table. Write the expressions in the correct columns.

Ways to express ...		
... apology	... warning	... thanks
Sorry	Look out!	

Now try these

1. a) Write down as many common expressions of surprise as you can.
   b) Write down three occasions when you might use these expressions.

2. a) Write down as many common expressions of refusal as you can.
   b) Write down three occasions when you might use these expressions.

Prefixes (2)

A **prefix** is a group of letters added to the
beginning of a word. A **prefix** changes
the meaning of a word in a particular way.

The prefix **mis** means **wrong**.

misspell

mislaid

Practice

Match the correct word to each picture.

misbehave	miscount	misdate	misadventure

1.

one, two, four, five...

2.

3.

4.

More to think about

Copy these words. Underline the prefix.
The first one has been done for you.

1. <u>mis</u>direct
2. misspell
3. misadventure
4. miscount
5. mislaid
6. misunderstand
7. misdate
8. misprint

Now try these

1. Write what you think these words mean.
   a) misspell
   b) misbehave
   c) misfortune
   d) misfire

2. Check your definitions of these words in a dictionary.
   Rewrite those that you got wrong.

3. Now make up three sentences. Use a **mis** word in
   each one.

Progress Test B

1. Write these words in alphabetical order.

   a)

   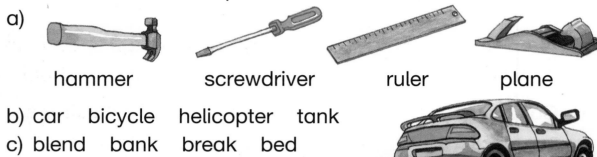

   hammer   screwdriver   ruler   plane

   b) car   bicycle   helicopter   tank
   c) blend   bank   break   bed

2. Write the words in the table in the correct columns.

   | wrist   tomb   wrong   knee   lamb   wriggle |
   | bomb   knight   wrinkle   numb   know   knife |

silent **b**	silent **k**	silent **w**

3. Write three words you might find in a dictionary between 'shake' and 'spear'.

4. Write two compound words for each of these words.
   a) snow
   b) foot
   c) fire
   d) some

5. Write an antonym for each of these words.

a) heavy   b) rough   c) leave   d) catch   e) empty
f) difficult   g) walk   h) sharp   i) huge   j) old

6. Complete each of these words using one of the suffixes **ly**, **ful** or **ness**.

a) slow _____   b) blind _____   c) help _____

d) use _____   e) glad _____   f) love _____

7) Copy the sentences. Choose the most suitable homonym to complete both sentences.

fair	wave	well	tie

a) Emma gave her mum a _____ from the boat.
A big _____ splashed over the boat.

b) The referee said it was a _____ tackle.
The _____ came to town.

c) I wear a _____ to school.
I can _____ up my shoe laces.

d) I did not feel _____.
You get water from a _____.

8. Copy these contractions. Put the missing apostrophes in the correct places.

a) Ill   b) weve   c) shes   d) hes   e) heres

f) isnt   g) wont   h) cant   i) havent   j) theyre

k) wed   l) youre   m) were   n) theyve   o) wheres

9. Write three common expressions for each everyday activity.

a) greeting someone

b) saying goodbye to someone

10. Write a sentence for each of these **mis** words.

| misprint | misfire | misdirected | misunderstood |

48